130 g of super SATs practice from CGP!

Geometry, Measures & Statistics questions can feel like a weighty part of the KS2 Maths SATs, but CGP is here to help — this Foundation SAT Buster is perfect for pupils who need some extra support.

It's packed with friendly practice on all the key skills, with hints, tips and step-by-step examples to walk them through the key methods.

There are also fun self-assessment boxes for each topic, plus a scoresheet to keep track of their overall marks. Trust CGP to lighten the load.

What CGP is all about

Our sole aim here at CGP is to produce the highest quality books — carefully written, immaculately presented and dangerously close to being funny.

Then we work our socks off to get them out to you — at the cheapest possible prices.

Published by CGP

Editors: Ruth Greenhalgh and Samuel Mann

ISBN: 978 1 78908 432 0

With thanks to Alison Griffin and Glenn Rogers for the proofreading.
Also thanks to Emily Smith for the copyright research.

Image of one pound coin used on page 28 © iStock.com/ LPETTET,
10 pence coins used on page 28 © iStock.com/john shepherd,
5 and 50 pence coins used on page 28 © iStock.com/duncan1890,
20 pence coin used on page 28 © iStock.com/Jaap2.

Printed by Elanders Ltd, Newcastle upon Tyne.
Clipart from Corel®

Based on the classic CGP style created by Richard Parsons.

Photocopying this book is not permitted, even if you have a CLA licence.
Extra copies are available from CGP with next day delivery.   •   **0800 1712 712**   •   **www.cgpbooks.co.uk**

Contents

Contents

Here's what you have to do...

In Year 6 you have to take some tests called the SATs. This book will help you do well in the geometry, measures & statistics questions on the maths tests.

This is a Trimeasuretops — it can handle even the trickiest maths questions.

Your aim is to become a Trimeasuretops.

Work through the questions in the book. When you finish a topic, add up your marks and write them in the scoresheet at the end of the book.

Then, put a tick in the box at the end of the topic to show how you got on.

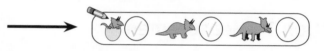

If you got a lot of questions wrong, put a tick in the circle on the left. Don't worry — every Trimeasuretops has to start somewhere. Make sure you know your geometry, measures and statistics rules inside out, then have another go.

If you're nearly there but your maths is still a bit wobbly, put a tick in the middle circle. Ask your teacher to help you work out the areas you need more practice on.

If you're really confident and got nearly all the questions right, tick the circle on the right.

Congratulations — you're a Trimeasuretops!

2D Shapes

> **Warm Up**
>
> *Take a look at this question first before you take on the rest.*
>
> 1) Look at the sequence below.
>   Draw the next shape in the empty box. Use a ruler.
>
>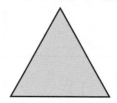

Have a go at this set of questions to test your knowledge of 2D shapes.

2) Fill in the missing entries in the table below.

Name of shape	Number of sides
....	3
Octagon	....
Pentagon	....

2 marks

3) Look at the shape to the right and then complete the sentence below.

   Side **A** is parallel to Side ....

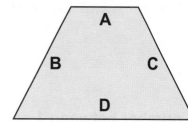

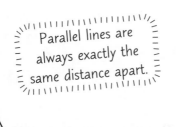

> Parallel lines are always exactly the same distance apart.

1 mark

4) Are these statements true or false? Circle the answers.

   A rectangle has four equal angles **and** four equal sides.   **TRUE / FALSE**

   An equilateral triangle has three equal angles.   **TRUE / FALSE**

2 marks

2D Shapes

5) The shapes below are labelled **A to D**. Put the letter for each shape in the correct place in the sorting diagram. One has been done for you.

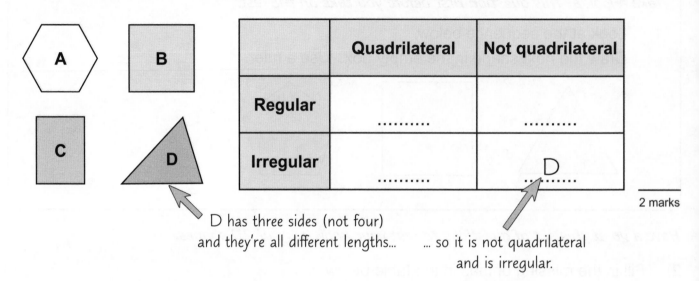

	Quadrilateral	Not quadrilateral
Regular	....	....
Irregular	....	D ....

2 marks

D has three sides (not four) and they're all different lengths...

... so it is not quadrilateral and is irregular.

6) Fill in the **missing side lengths** on the rectangle below.

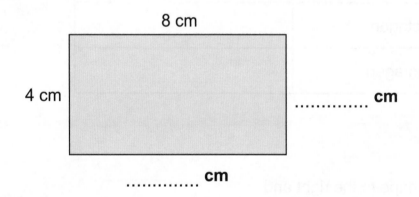

8 cm

4 cm

.... cm

.... cm

1 mark

7) Fill each gap with a **number between 1 and 6** to make the sentences correct. You can use a number more than once.

An isosceles triangle has .... equal sides and .... equal angles.

A parallelogram has .... sides and .... pairs of equal angles.

2 marks

Circles

Warm Up

Let's see if you're ready to answer some questions on circles.

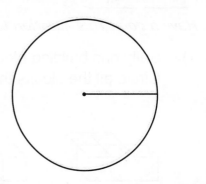

1) Measure the length of the radius of the circle.
   Write the length in cm inside the circle.

   The radius is the distance from the edge to the centre.

Test your knowledge of circles by doing the questions below.

2) Draw lines from the labels to the correct **part of the circle**.
   One has been done for you.

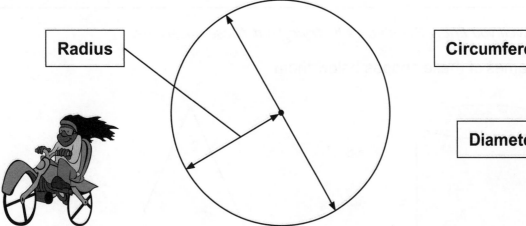

Radius

Circumference

Diameter

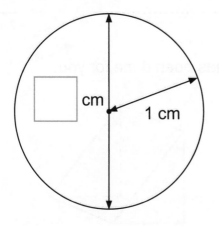

1 mark

3) Fill in the **missing lengths** on these circles.

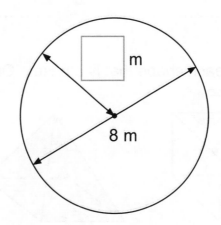

cm

1 cm

m

8 m

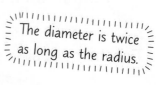
The diameter is twice as long as the radius.

2 marks

You need to know the parts of a circle to be a true Trimeasuretops. Do you think you're there yet?

© CGP — not to be photocopied

3D Shapes

Warm Up

Have a go at this question to ease you into 3D shapes.

1) Sally has building blocks that are two different shapes.
Circle all the blocks that are the same shape as the shaded one.

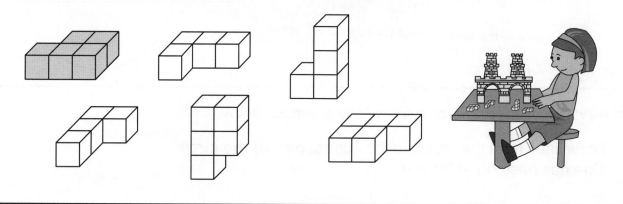

Now check how well you know 3D shapes by trying out these questions.

2) Write the names of these shapes below them.

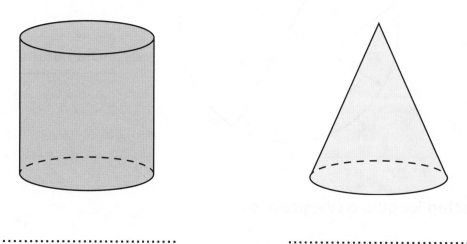

....

2 marks

3) Tick the box below each shape that is a prism. One has been done for you.

Both end faces
are the same, so
this a prism.

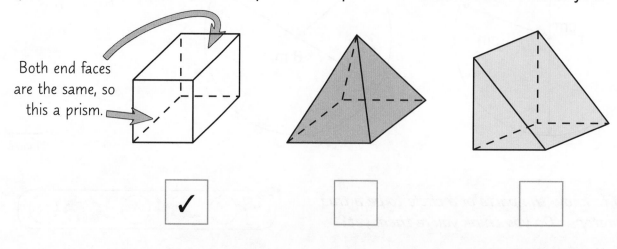

✓

1 mark

3D Shapes

4) **Match** each description to the shape it describes. One has been done for you.

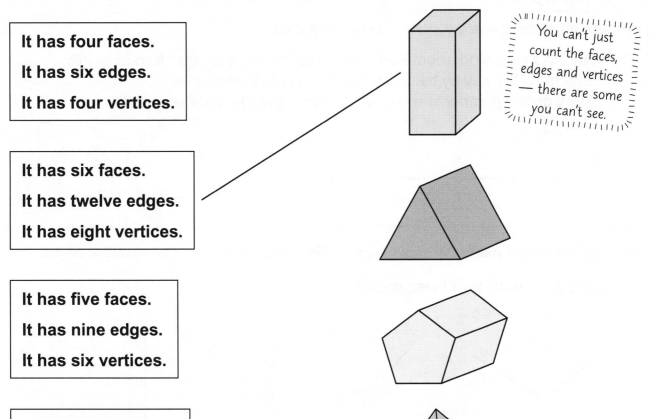

It has four faces.
It has six edges.
It has four vertices.

It has six faces.
It has twelve edges.
It has eight vertices.

It has five faces.
It has nine edges.
It has six vertices.

It has seven faces.
It has fifteen edges.
It has ten vertices.

You can't just count the faces, edges and vertices — there are some you can't see.

———
2 marks

5) Tick the box below all the nets that would make a **cube** when folded up.

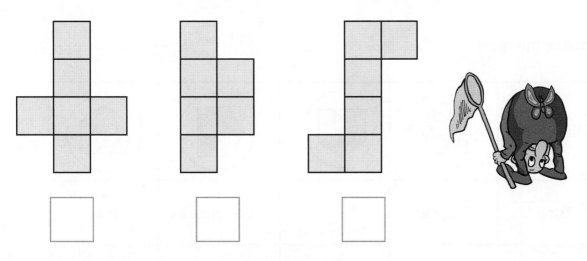

———
2 marks

No 3D shape can get in the way of a fully grown Trimeasuretops. How did you find these questions?

Angles

Warm Up

Have a go at this question and see how you get on.

1) Alyssa's clockwork robot walks one step for every quarter turn of its key.
   She turns the key by two full turns and lets the robot walk.
   Mark on the number line how many steps the robot walks.

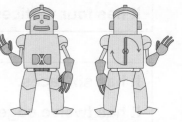

0   10

Let's see how much you know about angles. Try the questions on the next few pages.

2) Circle the **smallest** of these angles.

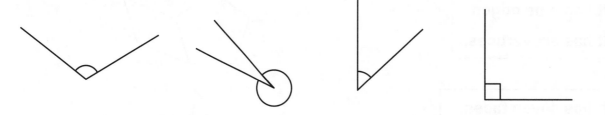

1 mark

How many of the angles are **larger** than a right angle?

1 mark

3) Complete the table.

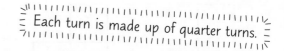
Each turn is made up of quarter turns.

Diagram	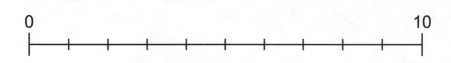			
Turn	Quarter	....	Three-quarter	Full
Number of degrees	90°	180°	....	....

2 marks

Angles

4) **Match** up these angle diagrams with their descriptions.
   One has been done for you.

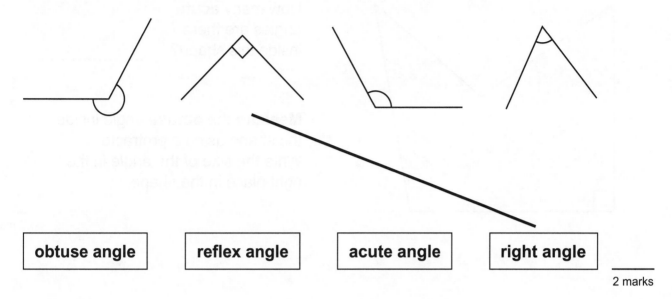

| obtuse angle | reflex angle | acute angle | right angle |

_____
2 marks

5) The angles in this shape are labelled **A to D**.

Write the letters of the angles in **order** of size,
starting with the smallest.

Do **not** measure the angles with a protractor.

smallest ⟶ largest

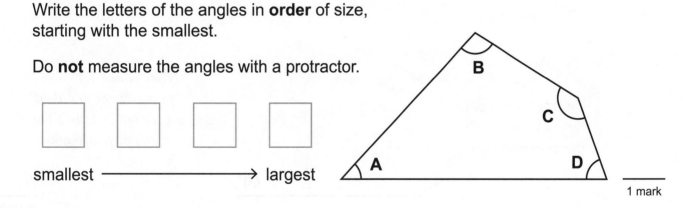

_____
1 mark

6) Measure this angle using the **protractor** shown below.

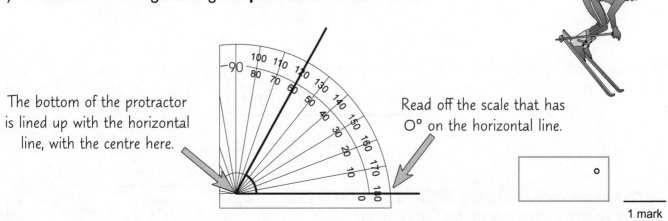

The bottom of the protractor
is lined up with the horizontal
line, with the centre here.

Read off the scale that has
0° on the horizontal line.

_____
1 mark

Angles

7) Look at the shape below.

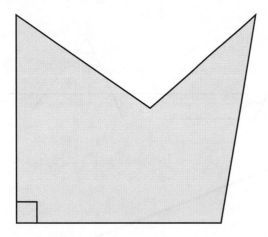

How many **acute** angles are there inside this shape? ....

Measure the **obtuse** angle inside the shape using a protractor. Write the size of the angle in the right place in the shape.

_____
2 marks

8) Use a ruler and a protractor to draw a **40°** angle and a **70°** angle from the lines below.

Line up the bottom line and centre of the protractor here.

Mark where 40° is on the protractor and then use a ruler to draw a line through your mark.

40°

_____
1 mark

70°

_____
1 mark

A Trimeasuretops knows the different types of angles and is handy with a protractor. How about you?

Angle Calculations

Warm Up

Take a look at this question to get you ready for some angle calculations.

coo-koo

1) How many degrees are there between the minute hand and the hour hand at the time shown on the clock?

☐ °

Solve these problems using the angle rules you know. You shouldn't use a protractor.

2) Work out the size of the missing angle **A** on the **straight line**.

   Show your working in the box.

130°

A

not drawn accurately

130° + A = 180° ⟵ Angles on a straight line always add up to 180°.

A = 180° − ....° = ...°

↗ Subtract the angle you know from 180° to find A.

A = ... °

2 marks

---

3) Work out the size of the missing angle **B** around the **point**.

   Show your working in the box.

160°

B

not drawn accurately

Remember there are 360° around a point.

B = ... °

2 marks

Angle Calculations

4) Work out the size of the missing angle **C** in the **triangle**.
The triangle is not drawn accurately.

Show your working in the box.

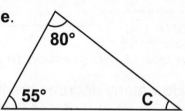

$$C + 80° + \text{..............}° = 180°$$ ← The angles in a triangle always add up to 180° — fill in the third angle.

$$C + \text{..............}° = 180°$$ ← Add up the angles you know.

$$C = 180° - \text{..............}° = \text{..............}°$$ ← Subtract the sum of these angles from 180°.

2 marks

5) Work out the size of the missing angle **x**.
Show your working in the box.

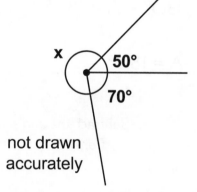

not drawn accurately

x = ... °

2 marks

Remember that a little square means an angle is a right angle.

6) Work out the size of the missing angle **y** in this shape.
The shape is not drawn accurately.

Show your working in the box.

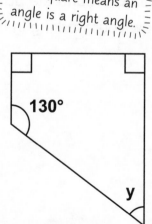

y = ... °

2 marks

Angle Calculations

7) Look at the diagram.
What is the size of angle **z**?

not drawn accurately

60°

z = ... °

_____
1 mark

8) Tommy has two toy swords hung on his wall, as shown.

Work out the size of angle **S**.

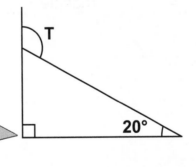

115°

not drawn accurately

S

S = ... °

_____
1 mark

9) Find the size of angle **T**.
The diagram is not drawn accurately.
Show your working in the box.

T

Fill in the size of this angle here.

20°

180° – 20° – .... ° = ... °

Subtract the angles you know from 180° to find the missing angle in the triangle.

T = ... ° – .... ° = ... °

Then use that angle to find T — they lie on a straight line.

T = ... °

2 marks

A Trimeasuretops always knows what to do when it comes to calculating angles. How did you do?

Coordinates

Warm Up

Are you ready for some questions on coordinates? Try this one first.

1) Padma and Kev are playing a game.

   Padma places three counters on the grid.
   Kev has to guess where they are.
   His guesses are B1, C3 and A2.

   How many guesses did he get right?

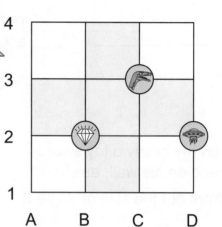

Now see how you do on these coordinate questions. The first one has been started.

2) Give the positions of the shapes on the grid.
   One has been done for you.

   Circle ....B2......   Triangle ....

   Square ....

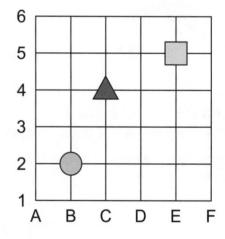

2 marks

3) Plot (2, 3), (5, 1) and (7, 5) on the grid below. One has been done for you.

(2, 3) means
2 across to the
right and 3 up
from (O, O).

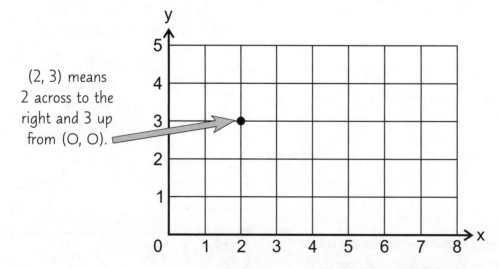

2 marks

Coordinates

4) Three vertices of a square are shown on the grid.

Plot the missing vertex and draw lines
to complete the square.

Give the coordinates of the vertex you drew.

Coordinates: (☐ , ☐)

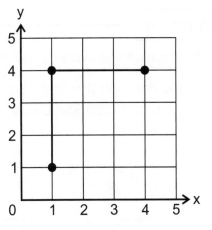

5) Match the letters of the points on the diagram to their coordinates.
One has been done for you.

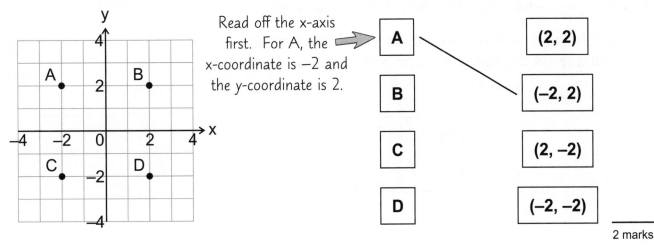

Read off the x-axis
first. For A, the
x-coordinate is −2 and
the y-coordinate is 2.

A		(2, 2)
B		(−2, 2)
C		(2, −2)
D		(−2, −2)

2 marks

6) The two rectangles in this
diagram are the same size.
Fill in the gaps to find the coordinates of point **A**.

To get from (0, 0) to (3, 2), you go

.... across to the right and .... up.

Doing the same from (3, 2):

x-coordinate of A = 3 + ... = ...

y-coordinate of A = 2 + ... = ...

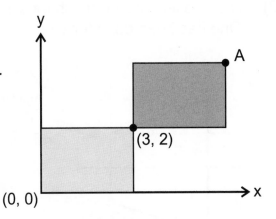

Coordinates: (☐ , ☐)

1 mark

Moving around a coordinate grid is easy for a real
Trimeasuretops. Are you a real Trimeasuretops yet?

© CGP — not to be photocopied

Section 1 — Geometry

Symmetry

Warm Up

Check how well you understand symmetry by trying this question.

1) Draw lines on the fruits below to show where they could be cut in half to give two identical pieces. Some may have more than one option.

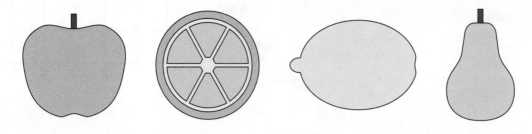

Now test your symmetry skills out on these questions.

2) Circle the shape with exactly two lines of symmetry.
Put a cross through the shape with no lines of symmetry.

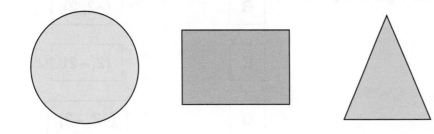

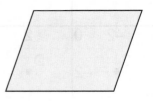

_____
2 marks

3) Draw reflections of the shapes in the dotted mirror line.
One has been done for you.

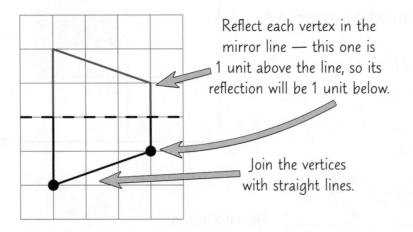

Reflect each vertex in the mirror line — this one is 1 unit above the line, so its reflection will be 1 unit below.

Join the vertices with straight lines.

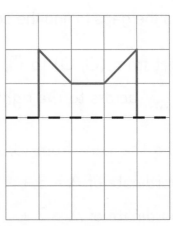

_____
1 mark

A Trimeasuretops can spot and draw lines of symmetry.
How do you feel about symmetry? Tick the box.

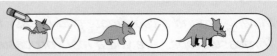

Translation and Reflection

Warm Up

Have a go at this question first before you take on the rest.

1) Draw a path along the grid lines for the diver to reach the treasure chest. The path must not cross any sea creatures or obstacles.

   Describe your path using the number of squares moved in each direction.
   (for example: 1 square right, 2 squares up)

   ....

   ....

   ....

Try these questions out and see how you get on translating and reflecting shapes.

2) Look at the shapes on this grid.

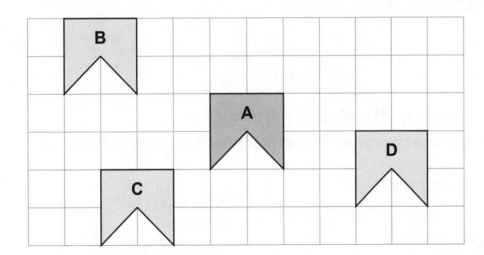

Some translations of shape **A** are described below.
Write the letter of the shape given by each translation.

3 squares left, 2 squares down   ....

4 squares right, 1 square down   ....

4 squares left, 2 squares up   ....

> You don't have to worry about the whole shape — just pick one vertex on A and follow the instructions to see where it ends up.

_____
2 marks

Translation and Reflection

3) Shape **X** is shown on the grid.

It is translated 5 squares right and 3 squares up.

Draw the new position of shape **X**.

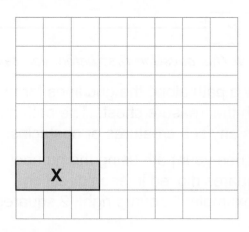

4) Reflect the shape on the grid below in the mirror line.

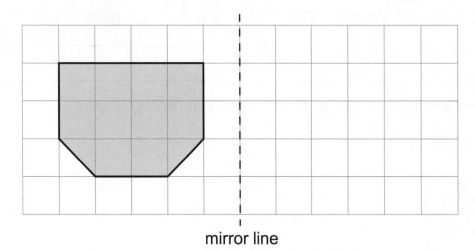

Reflect each vertex separately and then join them with straight lines.

mirror line

5) The shape on the grid is reflected in a mirror line.

What are the **new** coordinates of point **P** after the shape is reflected?

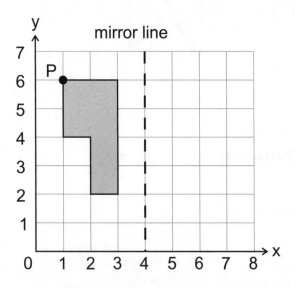

You might find it helpful to draw the position of the new shape on the grid.

Coordinates: (☐ , ☐)

Translation and reflection are a piece of cake for a fully grown Trimeasuretops. Do you feel the same?

Units

Warm Up

Have a go at this question to check you're happy with what different units measure.

1) Draw lines to **match** each unit to the quantity it measures.
    One has been done for you.

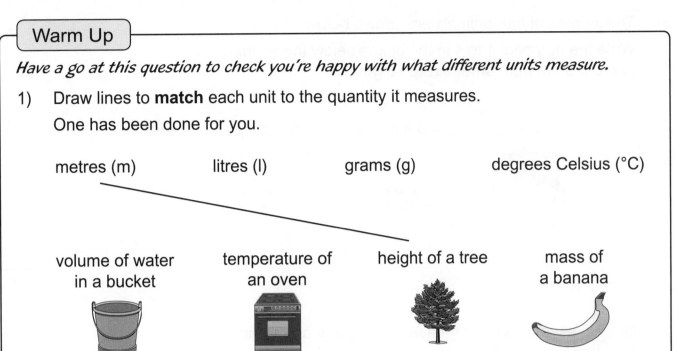

metres (m)   litres (l)   grams (g)   degrees Celsius (°C)

volume of water   temperature of   height of a tree   mass of
in a bucket   an oven   a banana

Now try these questions to really get to grips with using units and changing between them.

2) Put a tick in the box next to the **smaller** mass.

    5 kg [ ]   5 g [ ]

    _____
    1 mark

3) Circle the **best estimate** for each measurement. One has been done for you.

    The mass of a bicycle   12 g   (12 kg) ⟵ 12 g is very light — it's about the mass of a pen. A bicycle is quite heavy, so 12 kg is the best estimate.

    The length of a table   1 mm   1 m

    The volume of juice in a glass 250 ml   250 litres

    _____
    2 marks

4) Put a tick in the box next to the **larger** volume.

    Look carefully at the units.

    4 litres [ ]   10 ml [ ]

    _____
    1 mark

Units

5) The lengths of four animals are shown below.

Write the numbers 1 to 4 in the boxes below the animals to order them from **smallest to largest**.

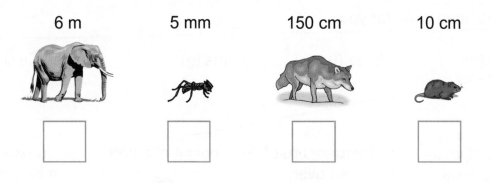

| 6 m | 5 mm | 150 cm | 10 cm |

☐ ☐ ☐ ☐

1 mark

6) Draw lines to match the measurements that are **equal**.
One has been done for you.

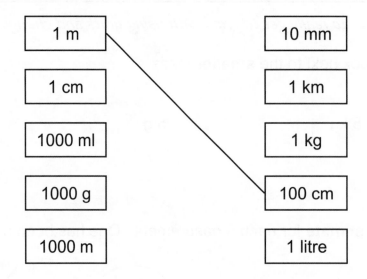

1 m		10 mm
1 cm		1 km
1000 ml		1 kg
1000 g		100 cm
1000 m		1 litre

2 marks

7) A tin contains **2 litres** of paint.
How many **millilitres** of paint are there?
This question has been done for you.

1 litre = 1000 ml ⟵ Write down the number of ml in 1 litre.

2 litres = 2 × 1000 ml = 2000 ml ⟵ Multiply by 2 to find the number of ml in 2 litres.

2000 **ml**

© CGP — not to be photocopied

8) A monkey weighs **6 kg**.
How much does the monkey weigh in **grams**?

.... **g** _____
1 mark

9) Jayden's calculator is **90 mm** long.
How long is the calculator in **cm**?

1 cm = ... mm 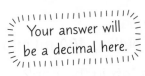 Write the number of mm in a cm here.

Then divide by that number to get the answer.

90 mm = 90 ÷ .... = ...

.... **cm** _____
1 mark

10) Taj is **140 cm** tall.
How tall is Taj in **metres**?

Your answer will be a decimal here.

.... **m** _____
1 mark

11) A bottle of oil has a capacity of **4000 ml**. It is **half full**.
How many **litres** of oil are there in the bottle?

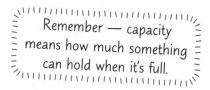

Remember — capacity means how much something can hold when it's full.

.... **litres** _____
1 mark

Section 2 — Measurement

Units

12) In a sports event, Sabira cycles **5 km** and then swims **100 m**.
How far does she travel in **total**, in **metres**?

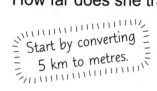
Start by converting
5 km to metres.

.... **metres** _____

13) A chef has **1.5 kg** of salt.
She shares the salt equally between **ten** pots.

How many **grams** of salt does she put in each pot?

.... **grams** _____

14) Darren has **3 litres** of soup in a pan.
He fills **seven** bowls with soup, putting **400 ml** into each bowl.

How many millilitres of soup are **left** in the pan?
Show your working in the box.

3 litres = 3 × .... = ... ml ⟵ Convert 3 litres to ml to find the number of ml in the pan at the start.

7 × 400 ml = ... ml ⟵ Next, find the total number of ml in 7 bowls of soup.

.... ml – .... ml = ... ml

⬆ Subtract the amount in 7 bowls from the original number of ml in the pan, to find the amount left over.

.... **ml**

Section 2 — Measurement   *© CGP — not to be photocopied*

Units

15) Shona has a strand of wool that is **4 metres** long.
She cuts the wool into **five** pieces.
Four of the pieces are each **90 cm** long.

How many centimetres long is the other piece?
Show your working in the box.

.... **cm**

2 marks

16) **1 kg** is approximately equal to **2 pounds**.

A baby weighs **4 kg**.
Approximately how many pounds does the baby weigh?
Circle the correct answer.

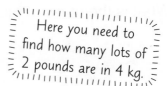
Here you need to find how many lots of 2 pounds are in 4 kg.

      2 pounds   **4 pounds**   **8 pounds**

1 mark

17) **8 km** is approximately equal to **5 miles**.

The distance between two villages is **24 km**. Approximately how
many miles apart are the villages? Show your working in the box.

8 km ≈ 5 miles ⟵ Use the conversion fact given in the question.

24 km = 8 km × .... ⟵ Write the number of 8's in 24 here...

... then multiply 5 miles by the same number.

≈ 5 miles × .... = ... miles

.... **miles**

2 marks

The Trimeasuretops can use all sorts of units.
Are you feeling happy with converting between units?

Reading Scales

Warm Up

Now you get to read scales showing different units. Try this one to get you started.

1) How much water is in this beaker? **Circle** the correct answer.

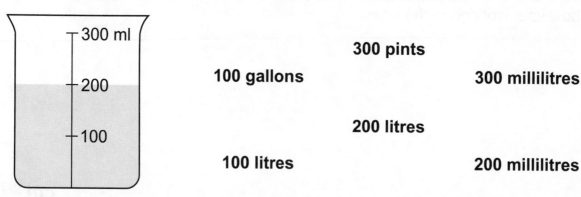

300 pints

100 gallons   **300 millilitres**

200 litres

100 litres   **200 millilitres**

Have a look at the question below to see how to read trickier scales, then do the rest yourself.

2) What is the mass of this apple? This question has been done for you.

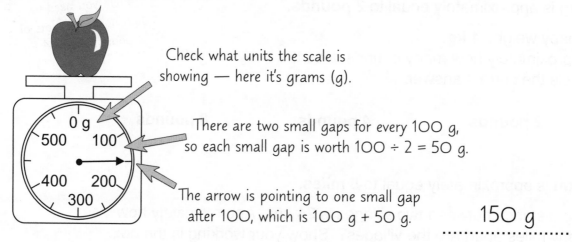

Check what units the scale is showing — here it's grams (g).

There are two small gaps for every 100 g, so each small gap is worth 100 ÷ 2 = 50 g.

The arrow is pointing to one small gap after 100, which is 100 g + 50 g.

150 g

3) How much milk is in this jug?

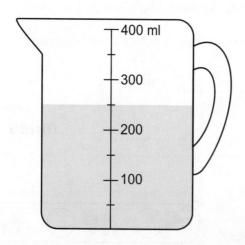

Start by working out what each small gap is worth.

.... **ml**

1 mark

Section 2 — Measurement   *© CGP — not to be photocopied*

Reading Scales

4) What is the mass of the pumpkin?

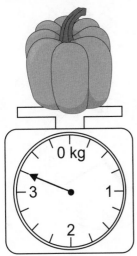

Each small gap is worth .... kg.

The arrow is pointing to

.... gap(s) after .... kg.

So the mass is .... kg.

.... **kg** ____

5) How many **centimetres** long is this fork?

The diagram is not drawn to actual size.

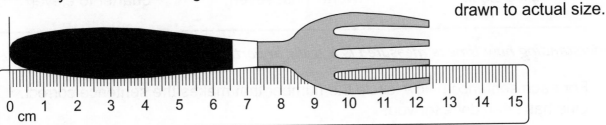

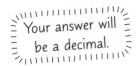

Your answer will be a decimal.

.... **cm** ____

1 mark

6) Amelie weighs a parcel she wants to post. The scales below show its **mass**.

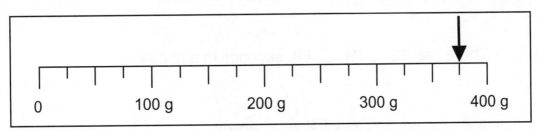

Amelie **removes** an item weighing **125 g** from the parcel.
What is the mass of the parcel **now**?

.... **g** ____

1 mark

Would you dare measure the Trimeasuretops? Tick one of the circles to show how you're feeling about scales.

© CGP — not to be photocopied

Section 2 — Measurement

Time

Warm Up

Have a go at this question on clocks to get you started on this topic.

1) Draw lines to **match** each clock below to the correct time.

six o'clock   twenty past seven   quarter to eleven

Understanding how time is measured is a really important real-life skill. Best get practising...

2) For each sentence below, circle the number that makes the sentence correct.
One has been done for you.

There are **12** /(**24**)/ **60** hours in a day.

There are **7** / **12** / **30** months in a year.

There are **28** / **30** / **31** days in October.

There are **12** / **24** / **60** seconds in a minute.

_____
2 marks

3) Write the time shown on the clock below in **words**.

> Remember — in Roman numerals,
> I means 1, V means 5 and X means 10.

....

_____
1 mark

Time

4) Write each time in the **12-hour clock** and circle 'am' or 'pm'.
One has been done for you.

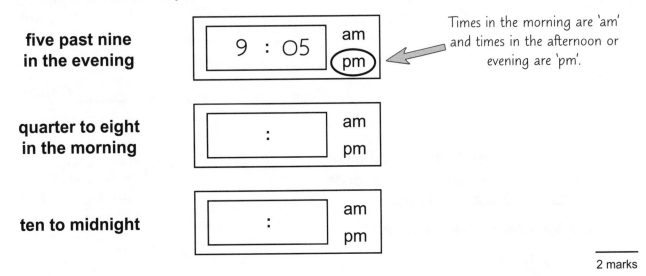

five past nine in the evening

9 : 05   am (pm)

Times in the morning are 'am' and times in the afternoon or evening are 'pm'.

quarter to eight in the morning

:   am pm

ten to midnight

:   am pm

2 marks

5) What time is shown on each 24-hour digital clock below?
Give your answer in **words**, including 'am' or 'pm'.
The first one has been done for you.

It's a time in the afternoon, so subtract 12 from 15 to find the hour.

15:25 .... twenty-five past three pm

20:45 ....

1 mark

6) The analogue clock below is **ten minutes slow**.
Which digital clock shows the **actual time**? **Tick** the box next to the correct one.

 9:55

 12:05

 10:15

1 mark

Section 2 — Measurement

Time

7) A baker ices **one cake every minute**.
How many cakes could he ice in **three hours**?

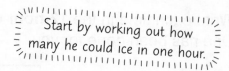
Start by working out how many he could ice in one hour.

............................cakes

1 mark

8) Clare and Hamish both run one mile.
Clare takes 7 minutes and 9 seconds.
Hamish is 12 seconds **faster**.

How long does it take Hamish?

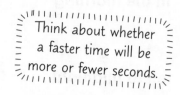
Think about whether a faster time will be more or fewer seconds.

..............minutes and ....seconds

1 mark

9) Ryan starts cleaning his house at **09:50**.
He cleans for **2 hours and 15 minutes**.

What time does Ryan **finish** cleaning? Give your answer in the 24-hour clock.

Time calculations are much easier if you split them into easy steps.

The last one will be the answer.

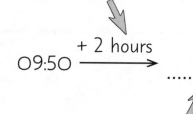

O9:5O   + 2 hours   →   ....   + 10 minutes   →   ....   + 5 minutes   →   ....

Fill in the time after each step.

....

1 mark

10) Yanika cooks a turkey for **3 hours and 15 minutes**.
She takes it out of the oven at **13:25**.

What time did she put it in the oven? Give your answer in the 24-hour clock.

....

1 mark

Time

11) The timetable shows the classes at a sports centre one afternoon.

Time	Sport
2.30 pm – 4 pm	Tennis
4 pm – 5 pm	Badminton
5 pm – 5.45 pm	Archery

Hannah went to the **tennis** and **archery** classes.

How much time did she spend doing sport that afternoon?
Give your answer in hours and minutes.

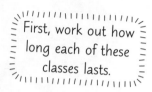
First, work out how long each of these classes lasts.

.... **hours and** .... **minutes** _____

1 mark

12) A bus timetable is shown below.

Rawley	11:45	12:15	12:45
Abchester	12:02	12:32	13:02
Claydon	12:36	13:06	13:36

How long does it take to travel from **Rawley** to **Abchester**?

You can use any column to work this out — it takes the same time whenever you set off.

.... **minutes** _____

1 mark

Jamil wants to travel from **Abchester** to **Claydon**.
He needs to be at Claydon by **1.30 pm**.

What is the **latest** time he can catch the bus from Abchester?
Give your answer in the 24-hour clock.

.... _____

1 mark

The Trimeasuretops hates being late so keeps its time skills up to scratch. How are you feeling about time?

Section 2 — Measurement

Money

Here's a question about coins to get you going — it's just like counting your pocket money.

1) Put a tick next to the set of coins that has the **greater** value.

 ☐    ☐

Money is really important in everyday life — have a go at these questions to build up your skills.

2) Change each amount from **pence to pounds**. One has been done for you.

220p = **£ 2 . 20**   175p = £   .   633p = £   .

————
1 mark

100p = £1,
so 220p = £2 and 20p

3) Change each amount from **pounds to pence**.

£3.50 = [   ] p   £8.95 = [   ] p   £1.09 = [   ] p

————
1 mark

4) Stacey buys a hat for **£7.50**. She pays with a **£10** note.
How much **change** does she get?

£ ....

————
1 mark

5) Pencils cost **35p** and rulers cost **£1.20**.
Nigel buys **two pencils** and **one ruler**. What does this cost?

£ ....

————
1 mark

A Trimeasuretops can always check it's been given the right change. How are your money skills?

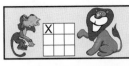

Perimeter and Area

Warm Up

Here's a gentle introduction to perimeter and area — you can just count the squares.

1) What is the perimeter and area of the grey shape?

Perimeter = ... **cm**

Area = ... **cm²**

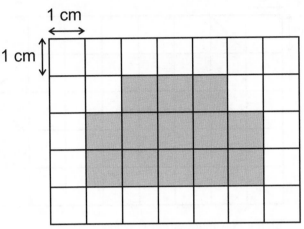

1 cm

1 cm

There's lots to do in this topic — but fear not, you'll be a perimeter and area whizz in no time.

2) What is the **perimeter** of this shape?

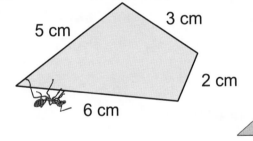

5 cm

3 cm

2 cm

6 cm

Not drawn to scale

Fill in the sides of the shape, then add them up.

5 cm + ... cm + ... cm + ... cm = ... cm

.... **cm**

1 mark

3) Use your **ruler** to find the **perimeter** of this triangle. Give your answer to the **nearest whole cm**.

Measure each side and then add the lengths together.

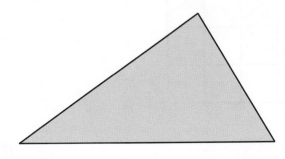

.... **cm**

1 mark

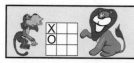

Perimeter and Area

4) The shapes below have been drawn on a 1 cm square grid.
What is the **area** of each shape? One has been done for you.

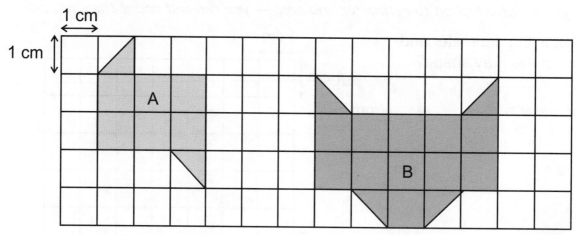

1 cm

1 cm

A

B

Shape A is made up of 6 whole
squares and 2 half squares.

Shape A: ....7....... cm²   Shape B: .... cm²

1 mark

5) A diagram of a pond is shown on this grid.
Each grid square represents a 1 metre square in real life.

Estimate the area of the pond.

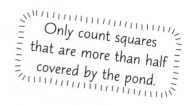

Only count squares
that are more than half
covered by the pond.

1 m

1 m

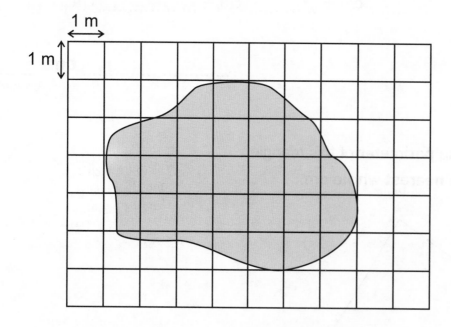

.... m²

1 mark

© CGP — not to be photocopied

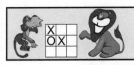

Perimeter and Area

6) Look at this rectangle.
It is not drawn to scale.

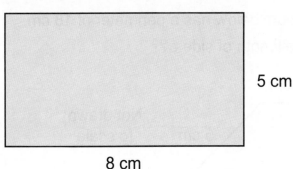

5 cm

8 cm

What is the **area** of the rectangle?

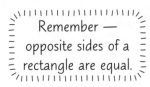

Area of a rectangle
= length × width

.... cm² ____

1 mark

What is the **perimeter** of the rectangle?

Remember —
opposite sides of a
rectangle are equal.

.... cm ____

1 mark

7) Find the perimeter of the shape below.
Show your working in the box.

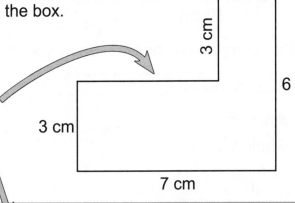

2 cm

3 cm

6 cm

Not drawn
to scale

You're not told the length
of one of the sides —
work this out first using
the other horizontal sides.

3 cm

7 cm

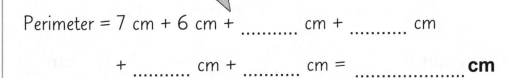

Missing side = 7 cm − .... cm = ... cm

Once you know all the sides, add them together to get the perimeter.

Perimeter = 7 cm + 6 cm + ... cm + ... cm

+ .... cm + ... cm = ... **cm**

2 marks

© CGP — not to be photocopied

Section 2 — Measurement

Perimeter and Area

8) The trapezium below has a perimeter of 18 cm.
What is the length of side **a**?

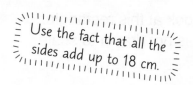
Use the fact that all the sides add up to 18 cm.

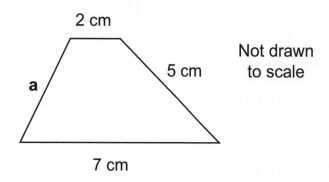

2 cm

5 cm

a

7 cm

Not drawn to scale

.... **cm** ____

1 mark

9) A tile is the shape of a square with side length 10 cm.
The tile has a white border and a grey square of side length 5 cm in the centre.

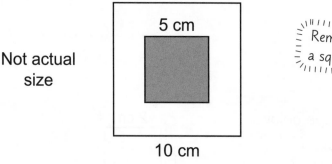

5 cm

Not actual size

10 cm

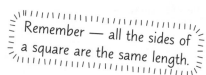
Remember — all the sides of a square are the same length.

What is the **area** of the **white** part of the tile? Show your working in the box

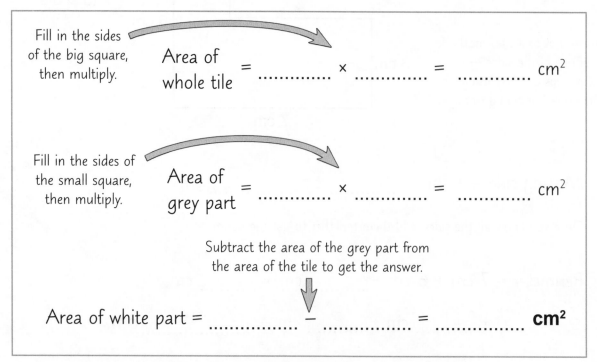

Fill in the sides of the big square, then multiply.

Area of whole tile = ... × .... = ... cm²

Fill in the sides of the small square, then multiply.

Area of grey part = ... × .... = ... cm²

Subtract the area of the grey part from the area of the tile to get the answer.

Area of white part = ... − .... = ... **cm²**

2 marks

Perimeter and Area

10) What is the **area** of this triangle?

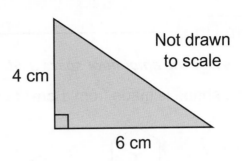

Not drawn to scale

4 cm

6 cm

Use the formula for the area of a triangle.

Area of triangle = $\frac{1}{2}$ × base × height

Area of triangle = $\frac{1}{2}$ × .... cm × .... cm   Fill in the values of the base and height here.

= .... cm^2 Then multiply to get the answer.

.... cm^2 _____

1 mark

11) What is the **area** of this triangle?

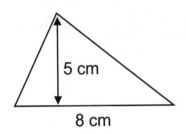

5 cm

8 cm

Not drawn to scale

.... cm^2 _____

1 mark

12) What is the **area** of this parallelogram?

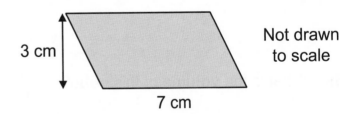

Not drawn to scale

3 cm

7 cm

Area of a parallelogram = base × height

.... cm^2 _____

1 mark

The Trimeasuretops loves doing perimeter and area questions. How do you feel about them?

Section 2 — Measurement

Volume

Volume is just the amount of space a 3D shape takes up. Try this question for starters.

1) This shape is made from **1 cm³ cubes**. Circle its **volume**.

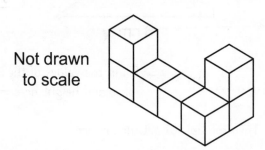

Not drawn to scale

8 cm³   **5 cm³**

6 cm³

7 cm³

9 cm³

Now have a go at finding the volume of cubes and cuboids in the next two questions.

2) What is the **volume** of this cuboid?

Use the formula for the volume of a cuboid.

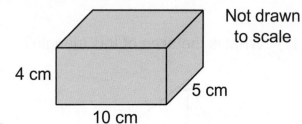

Not drawn to scale

4 cm

5 cm

10 cm

Volume of cuboid = length × width × height

Fill in the dimensions of the cuboid here.

Volume of cuboid = ... cm × .... cm × .... cm

= .... cm³ ⟵ Multiply to get the answer.

.... cm³

____
1 mark

3) What is the **volume** of this **cube**?

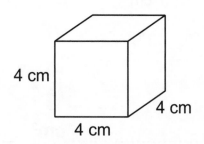

4 cm

4 cm

4 cm

Remember — all the edges of a cube are the same length.

.... cm³

____
1 mark

A Trimeasuretops can work out the volume of any cube or cuboid. Do you think you could do the same?

Tables, Charts and Graphs

Warm Up

Try out this question first before you take on the rest.

1) Greg wrote a list of the objects he saw at the beach.

   Use his list to fill in the tally chart.

   fossil, fossil, seashell, fossil, mermaid's purse, seashell, seashell, fossil, seashell, mermaid's purse, seashell, fossil, seashell, fossil, seashell, seashell

Object	Tally	Frequency
Seashell		
Fossil		
Mermaid's purse		

Take a look at these questions to see the different ways data can be organised.

2) Savi went fishing and recorded the number of different types of fish she caught.

   She put her results in a bar graph.

The scale is going up in steps of 2.

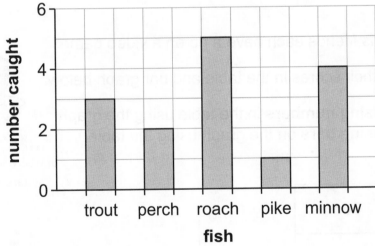

Which type of fish did Savi catch the **most** of?

.... _____

1 mark

Are these statements true or false? Circle the answers.

Savi caught **more** trout than she did minnows.   TRUE / FALSE

Savi caught **twice** as many perch as she did pike.   TRUE / FALSE _____

2 marks

Tables, Charts and Graphs

3) Niamh grew three different types of flowers.

She recorded how many of each type she grew and put her data into the table on the right.

Use the table to fill in the **pictogram** below.

Flower	Number of flowers
sunflower	4
marigold	9
sweet pea	7

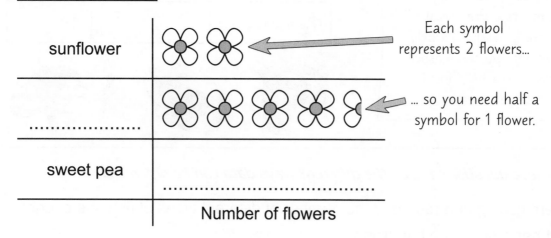

= 2 flowers

Each symbol represents 2 flowers...

... so you need half a symbol for 1 flower.

Number of flowers

2 marks

4) Ahmed and his friends each have a go on a video game.

He recorded their scores in the table and bar graph below.

Fill in the **missing numbers** in the table using the graph.
Draw the **missing bars** on the graph using the table.

Start by working out what score one square represents on the graph.

Player	Score
Ahmed	30
Sophia	....
Kelly	....
Ashton	35

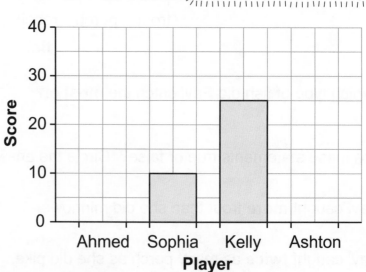

2 marks

Tables, Charts and Graphs

5) The line graph below shows the number of visitors to a castle in five days.

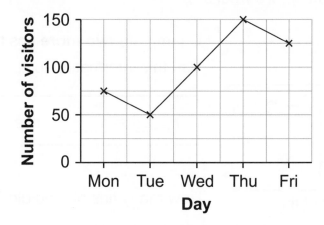

How many visitors were there on **Tuesday**?

.... **visitors**

How many **more** visitors were there on **Friday** than on **Wednesday**?

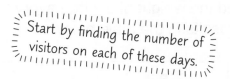

Start by finding the number of visitors on each of these days.

.... **visitors**

2 marks

6) A shopkeeper plotted the line graph below using data from the table.

Month	Number of toys sold
September	30
October	40
November	20
December	70
January	10

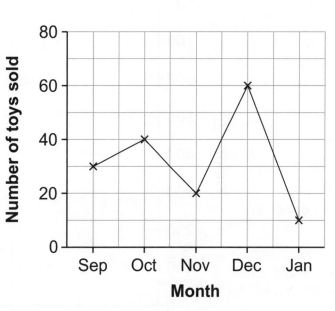

Circle the point on the graph that has been plotted **incorrectly**.

1 mark

Tables, Charts and Graphs

7) Aidan drew a pictogram to show the number of tins of food his pets ate in two weeks.

Brutus	🦴🦴
Twinkle	🦴🦴🦴🦴
Champ	🦴🦴

Number of tins

Champ ate **two more** tins than Brutus. Use this information to fill in the **key**.

 = ... tins

1 mark

How many tins of food did **Twinkle** eat?

.... **tins**

1 mark

8) A vet recorded the weight of a kitten every **two weeks** from when it was born. She put her results in the table below.

Week	0	2	4	6	8
Weight (g)	100	200	350	600	700

Plot these results as a **line graph** on the axes below.
The first two points have been plotted for you.

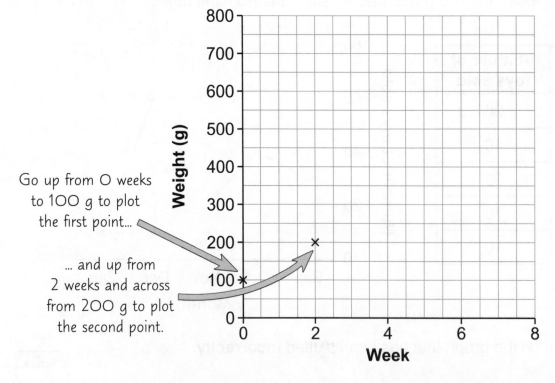

Go up from 0 weeks to 100 g to plot the first point...

... and up from 2 weeks and across from 200 g to plot the second point.

Don't forget to join up your points with straight lines at the end.

2 marks

Tables, Charts and Graphs

9) Two racing tortoises were placed next to a starting post and let go.

   Their distance away from the post was recorded every minute for ten minutes.

   The results were used to draw the graph below.

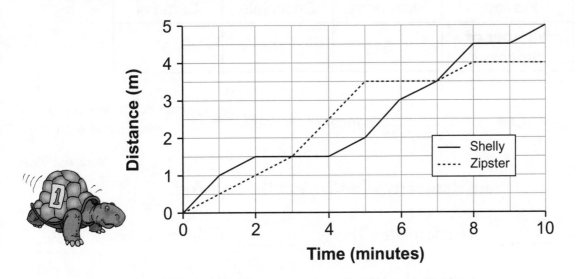

Which tortoise was the **first** to reach **1 m** away from the post?

Read across from 1 m on the vertical axis and see which line you hit first.

....

How far from the post was **Zipster** after **5 minutes**?

.... m

2 marks

10) Liz asked 24 people what their favourite sport is.
    She recorded her results in the pie chart below.

What was the **most popular** sport?

....

How many people's favourite sport was **tennis**?

Decide what fraction of the circle represents 'Tennis' and work out this fraction of the total number of people.

.... **people**

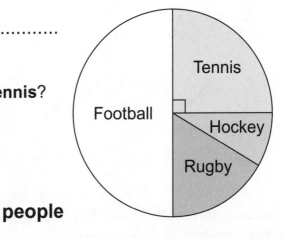

2 marks

Tables, Charts and Graphs

11) The table below shows the numbers of different cupcakes at a party.

Complete the **pie chart** below using the information from the table.

Flavour	Strawberry	Chocolate	Caramel
Number of cupcakes	5	10	5

There are 5 + 10 + 5 = ... cupcakes in total. ⟵ Find how many cupcakes there are in total.

5 out of .... are strawberry. This is $\frac{1}{4}$ of the cupcakes. Work out what fraction of the total each flavour is.

10 out of .... are chocolate. This is .... of the cupcakes.

5 out of .... are caramel. This is .... of the cupcakes.

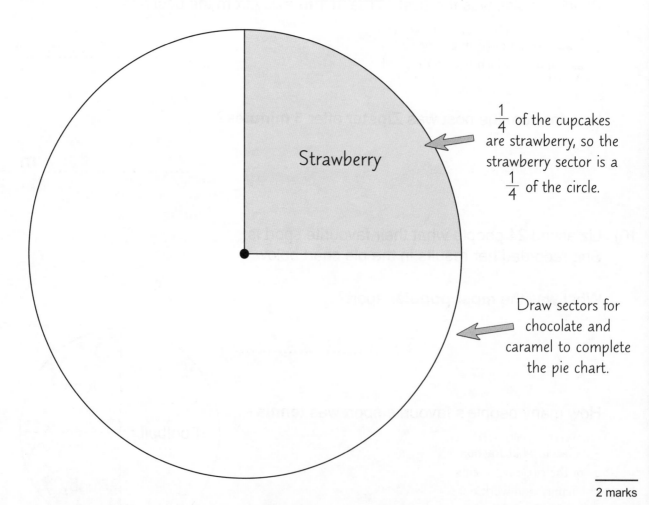

$\frac{1}{4}$ of the cupcakes are strawberry, so the strawberry sector is a $\frac{1}{4}$ of the circle.

Draw sectors for chocolate and caramel to complete the pie chart.

2 marks

A Trimeasuretops has no problems plotting graphs.
Do you feel the same? Tick the box.

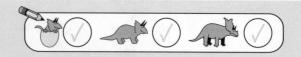

Analysing Data

Warm Up

Have a go at this question to get you ready to analyse some data.

1) Clark has 5 toy cars, Mick has 3 and Priya has 7.

   If they shared their toy cars out equally between them,
   how many would they each have? Circle the correct answer.

   3   5   15   4   7

Try the questions below to see how well you do at analysing data.

2) Fred and Olga counted the vehicles they saw on two different roads.

   They recorded their results in the **tally chart** below.

	Fred	Olga
Car	ⅢⅠⅠ	ⅢⅢ
Bike	ⅢⅠ	ⅠⅠ
Van	ⅠⅠⅠ	ⅠⅠⅠⅠ

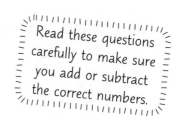

Read these questions carefully to make sure you add or subtract the correct numbers.

How many **vans** did Fred and Olga see **in total**?

.... **vans**

How many **vehicles** did **Olga** see in total?

.... **vehicles**

How many **more** bikes did Fred see than Olga?

.... **bikes**

3 marks

Analysing Data

3) The bar chart below shows the eye colours of pupils in **two different classes**.

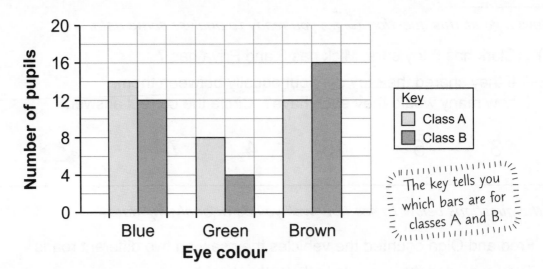

The key tells you which bars are for classes A and B.

Which eye colour is **most** common in class **A**?

....

Which class had the most pupils with **green eyes**?

Class ....

How many pupils are there in total in class **B**?

.... **pupils** ____

3 marks

4) Mei and four of her friends played football.
The number of goals they each scored were:

4   1   3   7   5

Work out the **mean** number of goals scored.

Total = ... + ... + ... + ... + ... = ... ← Work out how many goals were scored in total.

.... ÷ 5 = ... ← There are five people, so divide the total by 5 to find the mean.

.... **goals** ____

1 mark

Analysing Data

5) Franco was given **8** homework exercises in **4** weeks.

Work out the **mean** number of homework exercises he was given per week.

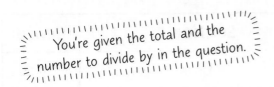
You're given the total and the number to divide by in the question.

.... **exercises**

6) Chloe has **three** money bags. The mean amount in each bag is **£4**.

How much money is in the bags in **total**?

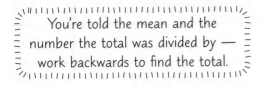
You're told the mean and the number the total was divided by — work backwards to find the total.

£........................

1 mark

7) Nev measured the temperature in his garden for **five** days.
He recorded his results in this table. The temperature for **Day 4** is missing.

Day	1	2	3	4	5
Temperature (°C)	10	7	8		3

The mean temperature was **6 °C**.

What was the temperature on **Day 4**? Show your working in the box.

10 + 7 + 8 + 3 = ...   ⟵ Work out the total without Day 4.

6 × 5 = ...   ⟵ Find the actual total by multiplying the mean by the number of days.

Subtract to get the temperature on Day 4. ➦   .... − .... = ... **°C**

2 marks

Analysing data is great fun for a Trimeasuretops.
Tick the box to show how you found it.

Scoresheet

Fill in the score sheet below as you go through the book.
When you're finished with a section, work out your total marks to see how you're doing.

Section 1	Score
2D Shapes	/ 10
Circles	/ 3
3D Shapes	/ 7
Angles	/ 12
Angle Calculations	/ 14
Coordinates	/ 9
Symmetry	/ 3
Translation and Reflection	/ 5
Total for Section 1	**/ 63**

Section 2	Score
Units	/ 20
Reading Scales	/ 4
Time	/ 14
Money	/ 4
Perimeter and Area	/ 14
Volume	/ 2
Total for Section 2	**/ 58**

Section 3	Score
Tables, Charts and Graphs	/ 20
Analysing Data	/ 11
Total for Section 3	**/ 31**

Total for Book	**152**

Look at your total score to see how you're doing and where you need more practice:

0 – 79 — Don't worry if you got lots wrong. Revise the skills that you're struggling with and then have another go.

80 – 119 — You're doing well. Take a look back at any sections you're struggling with and have another go to make sure you're happy.

120 – 152 — You're doing really well. Give yourself a pat on the back.